It's Easy To P
Delta Goodrem

Wise Publications
part of The Music Sales Group

London / New York / Paris / Sydney / Copenhagen / Berlin / Madrid / Tokyo

Published by
Wise Publications
8/9 Frith Street, London W1D 3JB, England.

Exclusive Distributors:
Music Sales Limited
Distribution Centre, Newmarket Road, Bury St Edmunds, Suffolk IP33 3YB, England.
Music Sales Pty Limited
120 Rothschild Avenue, Rosebery, NSW 2018, Australia.

Order No. AM89442
ISBN 0-7119-3031-7
This book © Copyright 2004 by Wise Publications.

Music arranged by Jon Paxman.
Music processed by Paul Ewers Music Design.
Cover photograph: Bob King / Redferns.
Printed in the United Kingdom by Caligraving Limited, Thetford, Norfolk.

Your Guarantee of Quality
As publishers, we strive to produce every book to the highest commercial standards.
The music has been freshly engraved and the book has been carefully designed to
minimise awkward page turns and to make playing from it a real pleasure.
Particular care has been given to specifying acid-free, neutral-sized paper made from
pulps which have not been elemental chlorine bleached.
This pulp is from farmed sustainable forests and was produced with special regard for the environment.
Throughout, the printing and binding have been planned to ensure a sturdy,
attractive publication which should give years of enjoyment.
If your copy fails to meet our high standards, please inform us and we will gladly replace it.

www.musicsales.com

Blue Berceuse

Track 5/13

MIKE CORNICK

Bass lead-in (even quavers)

Born To Try

Words & Music by Delta Goodrem & Audius Mtawarira

1. Do-ing ev-'ry-thing that I__ be-lieve__
2. No point in talk-ing what should

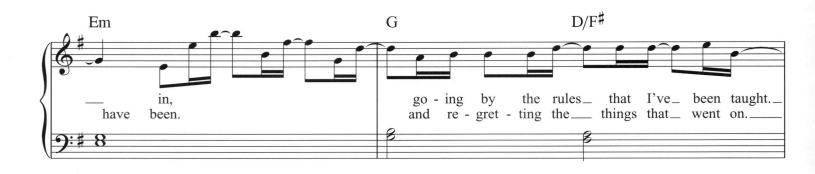

__ in,
have been.

go-ing by the rules__ that I've__ been taught.__
and re-gret-ting the__ things that__ went on._____

More un-der-stand-ing__ of what's__
Life's full of mis-takes,__ des -

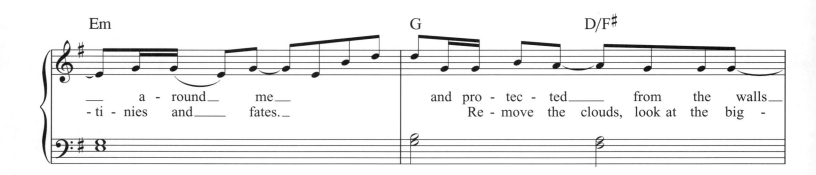

__ a-round__ me__
-ti-nies and__ fates.__

and pro-tec-ted____ from the walls__
Re-move the clouds, look at the big -

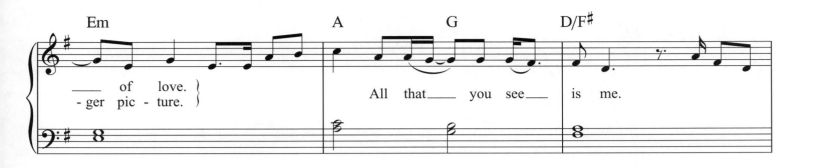

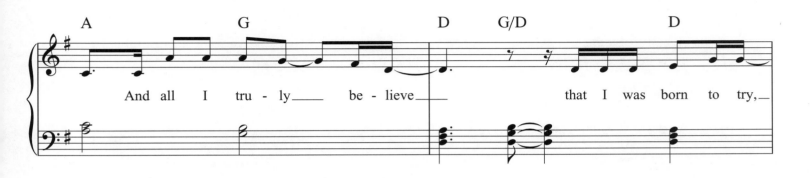

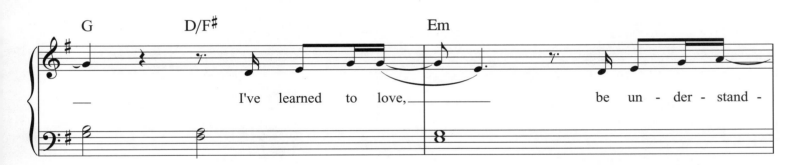

Butterfly

Words & Music by Gary Barlow, Eliot Kennedy & Tim Woodcock

9

10

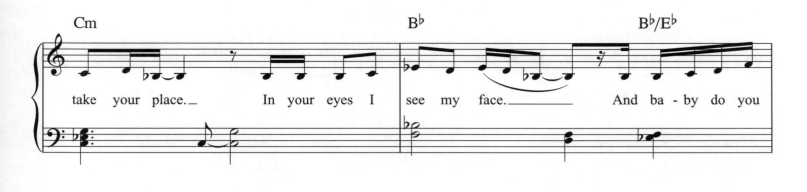

take your place._ In your eyes I see my face.____ And ba - by do you

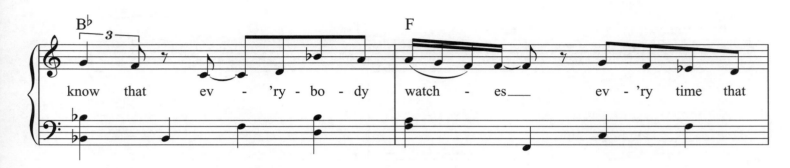

know that ev - 'ry - bo - dy watch - es__ ev - 'ry time that

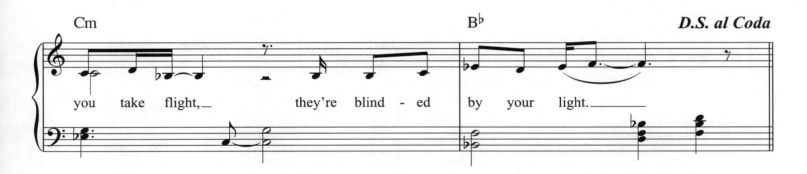

D.S. al Coda

you take flight,_ they're blind - ed by your light._____

⊕ Coda

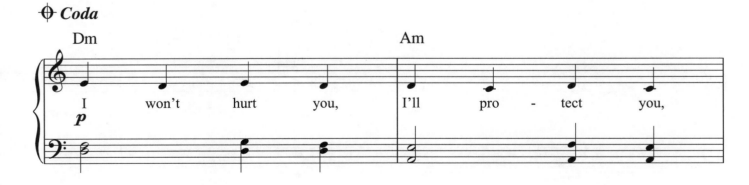

p

I won't hurt you, I'll pro - tect you,

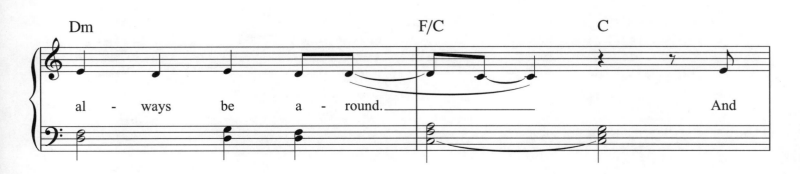

al - ways be a - round._____ And

In My Own Time

Words & Music by Delta Goodrem

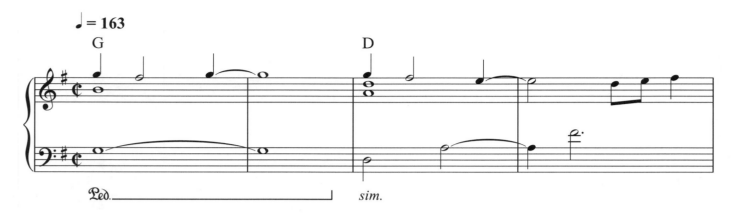

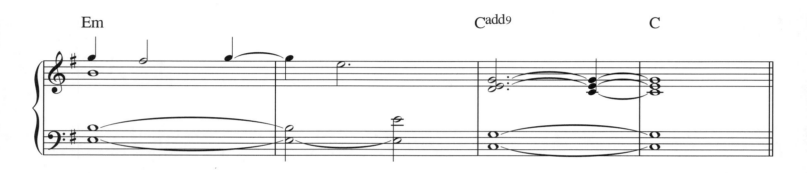

melody throughout set 1 octave higher

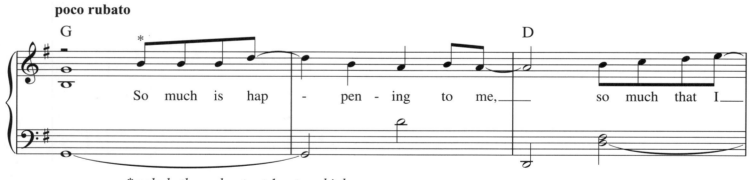

So much is hap - pen - ing to me,___ so much that I___

___ can't ev - en see, so ma - ny words___ of wis - dom that

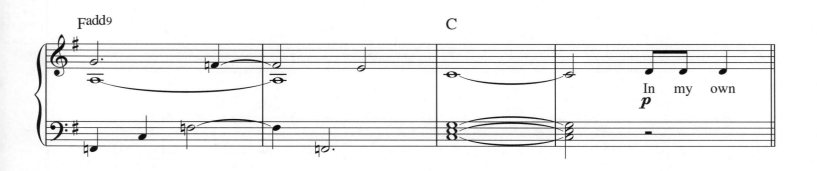

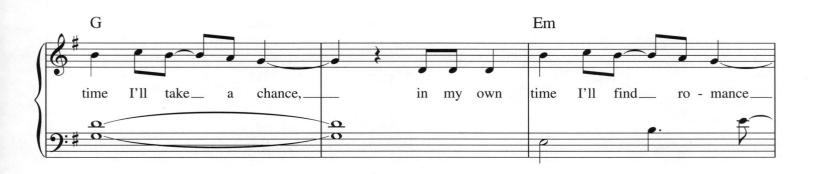

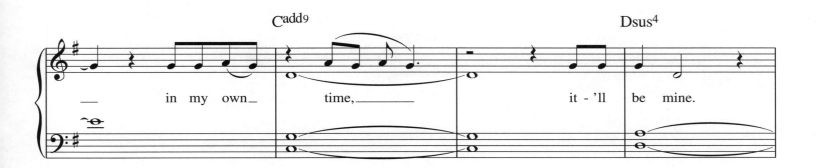

19

20

Innocent Eyes

Words & Music by Delta Goodrem & Vince Pizzinga

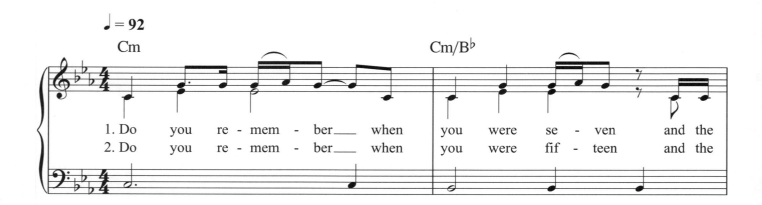

1. Do you re‑mem‑ber___ when you were se‑ven and the
2. Do you re‑mem‑ber___ when you were fif‑teen and the

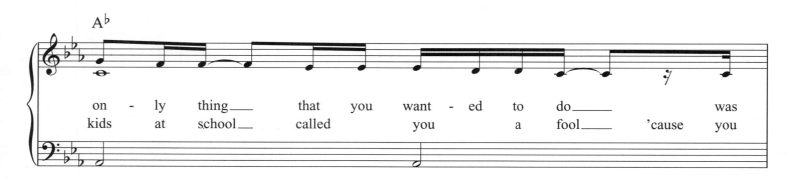

on‑ly thing___ that you want‑ed to do___ was
kids at school___ called you a fool___ 'cause you

show your mum___ that you could play the pi‑a‑no?
took the chance___ to dream? In the

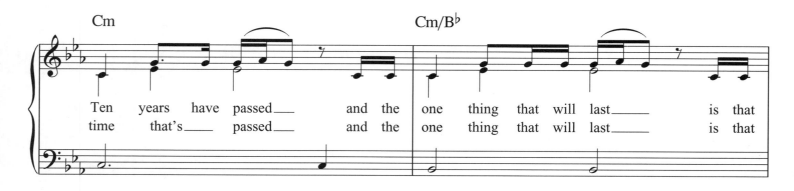

Ten years have passed___ and the one thing that will last___ is that
time that's___ passed___ and the one thing that will last___ is that

Predictable

Words & Music by Delta Goodrem, Kara DioGuardi & Jarrad Rogers

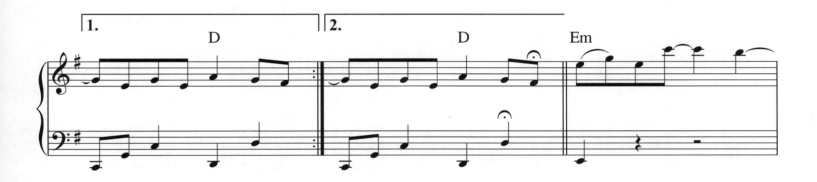

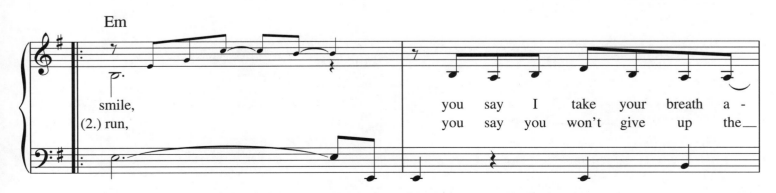

smile,
(2.) run,

you say I take your breath a-
you say you won't give up the__

28

Lost Without You

Words & Music by Matthew Gerrard & Bridget Benenate

1. I know I can be a lit-tle stub-born some-times, and I'd say a lit-tle right-eous and too proud. I just wan-na find a way to com-pro-mise

2. How'm I ev-er gon-na get rid of these blues? Ba-by I'm so lone-ly all the time. Ev-'ry-where I go I get so con-fused,

34

Not Me, Not I

Words & Music by Delta Goodrem, Kara DioGuardi,
Gary Barlow, Eliot Kennedy & Jarrad Rogers

D.S. al Coda

Throw It Away

Words & Music by Gary Barlow, Eliot Kennedy & Cathy Dennis

♩ = 136 with swing

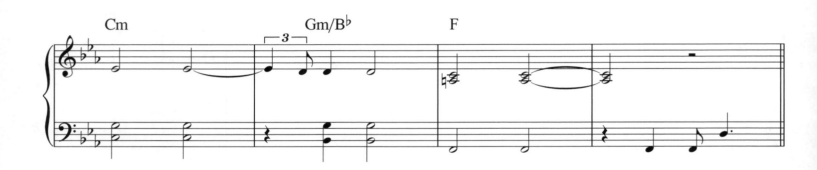

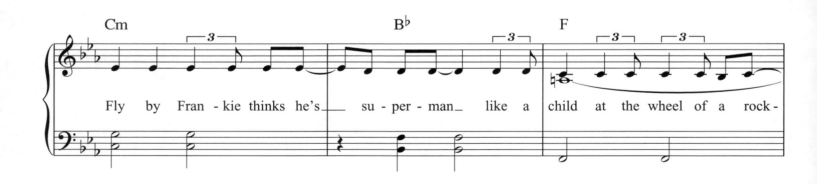

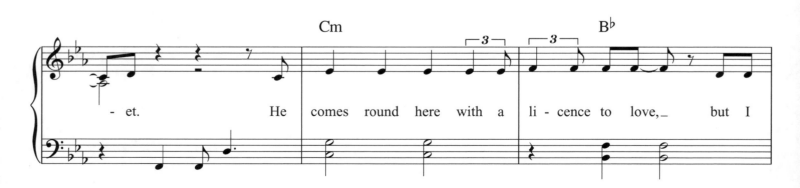

42

43

Repeat and fade vocal ad lib.

47

Will You Fall For Me

Words & Music by Delta Goodrem

To Coda ⊕

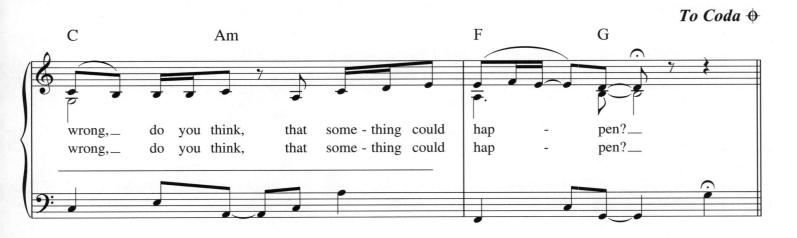

49

50

A Year Ago Today

Words & Music by Delta Goodrem, Mark Holden & Paul Wiltshire

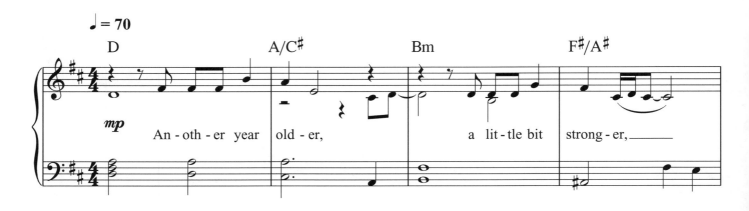

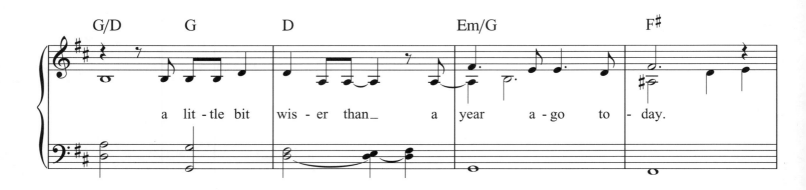

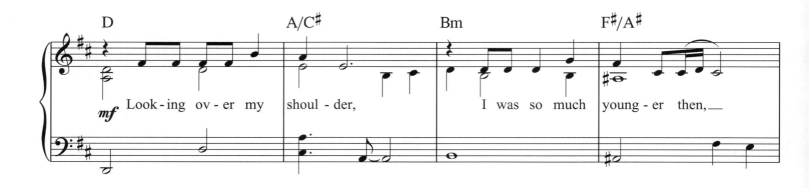

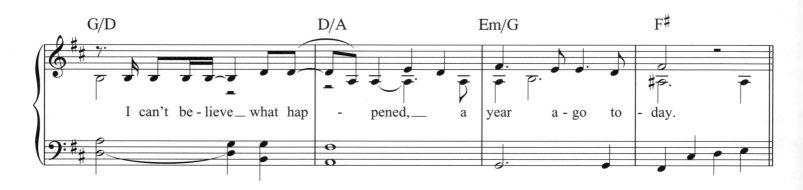

1. And I just can't for - get a - bout it, _____
2. And I just can't _____ un - der - stand _____ it, _____

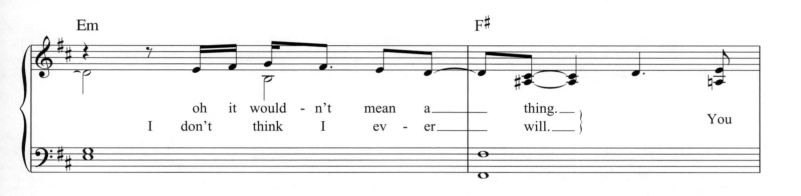

oh it would - n't mean a _____ thing. _____
I don't think I ev - er _____ will. ___

You

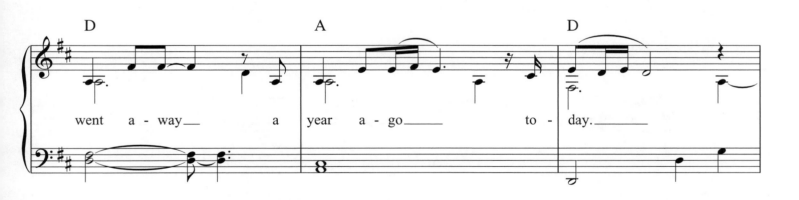

went a - way ___ a year a - go _____ to - day. _____

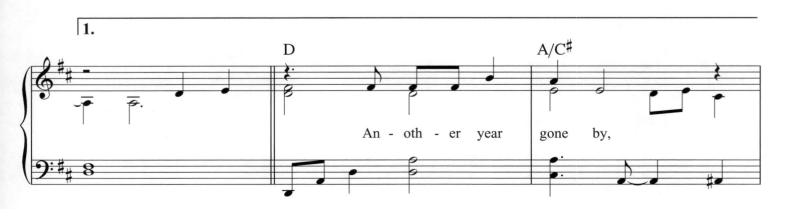

1.

An - oth - er year gone by,

oh, the tears have run dry,_____ life seemed__ so un-

- kind, a year a - go to - day. And

how ma - ny times__ have I quest - ioned my - self,_____

what__ more__ could I do?_____ And

how ma - ny times__ have I fooled my - self,_____